INTRODUCTION

G000114380

Chillies have been a fascination to people for millennia. First domesticated around 7,000 years ago in Ecuador, they have since spread across the globe and today there is no more ubiquitous a flavouring, with the exception of salt.

Chillies are used around the world for cooking, ornamentally and even made into pest controls and military products, such as pepper spray. There are some 4,000 varieties around the world. They range in heat from the mildest of bell peppers to the superhots of the world that measure in excess of 2 million Scoville units. That means one part chilli is still detectable in 2 million parts water!

Colours range from lime or racing green to yellow, gold, orange, white, purple and red, bi-colur and tri-colour, sometimes all on the same plant. Chillies appear in a wide array of shapes and sizes from the tiny round Chiltepin to elongated Pasilla pods that can reach 30cm; long and thin, fat and round, wedges, bullets, spirals, mushroom, heart or star-shaped. With new varieties bred every year, the world of chillies is a growing fascination to gardeners and chefs alike.

Chillies are integral to American, Asian, southern African and even European cuisine; it is difficult to conceive of global food culture without them. They are eaten raw, cooked into curries, stuffed, roasted, dried, smoked, pickled, sauced and processed for a huge range of uses and flavours.

We hope that you will enjoy this introduction to the captivating world of chillies!

HISTORY OF CHILLIES

Chillies are native to Central America and archaeologists have discovered that people were eating them as far back as 7,500BC. Amerindians began farming them from around 5,000BC making them one of the oldest domesticated plants in the world. The name 'chilli' comes from the Nahuatl language, spoken in the highlands of Mexico.

It is not surprising then, that the Mexicans have the most sophisticated of chilli cultures, with a huge range of fresh, smoked, dried and pickled chillies as well as powders and blends of powders, known as Moles. Chillies are used as much for their range of flavours as they are for their heat.

By 1,000BC, Mayans were making the first chilli sauces, using them to flavour tortillas. By 100 BC, they were

processing chillies in various ways including smoking them to make Chipotles, which are still popular today, with their rich, smoky flavour.

When the Spanish arrived in the late 1400s, South America's chilli production was booming. According to a Spanish chronicler, there were "hot green chillies, smoked chillies, water chillies, tree chillies, flea chillies, sharp, pointed red chillies."

Mayans and Aztecs categorized chillies not only by heat, but also the type of heat; a quick, sharp explosion that quickly subsides, or a broad building heat that lingers.

The Aztecs didn't confine chillies to their food, they used them in a number ways: to flavour chocolate drinks; inhaled as a punishment; mixed with urine and used as a face

cream and paid to Aztec Emperors as an early form of tax.

After 9,000 years of use in Central America, chillies were suddenly discovered by European explorers and so began their dispersion around the world. When Christopher Columbus was introduced to the spicy pods, he assumed they were part of the Black Pepper family and named them Red Peppers; a mistake but a name that has stuck.

Even though Columbus brought chillies eastwards to Europe for the first time, few Europeans actually heard about them. It was to the Portuguese that the major spread of chillies around the world can be attributed.

Chillies travelled across the Atlantic to Africa with Portuguese ships and in 50 years, they had made it around the

Cape of Good Hope to India. They were quickly incorporated into Indian cuisine, perhaps because people were already used to pungent flavourings.

It is also interesting to note that around the world, the poorer the diet, the more popular chillies are. Chillies are a cheap and easy way to introduce intense flavour to food. They also cause endorphins to be released in the body, so producing a kind of "fake enjoyment" of the food.

Chillies travelled aboard trade ships to northern Africa and slave ships to Mozambique. Today, they are a major part of the cuisine of southern Africa and grow wild across the region. By the 1530s, ships were circumnavigating the globe in the opposite direction, sailing around Cape Horn, across the Pacific to Indonesia, taking chillies with them.

From these major locations, chillies spread along regional trade routes around Asia, China and back into Europe. Until the 19th century, Europeans thought that chillies originated in India because they had come from the east. It might be assumed that chillies reached North America directly from Mexico but in actual fact, they took a very convoluted route, being introduced by European slave traders in the early 17th century. Even then, they were not widely popular, being grown mainly as a cheap flavouring to support the diets of African slaves.

Today, chillies are the world's most popular flavouring, with the possible exceptions of salt and pepper. There are now some 4,000 varieties grown worldwide and a continuous stream of new cultivars. The popularity of chillies continues to spread worldwide amongst horticulturists as well as chefs.

Chillies have even spawned their own fan-clubs with 'chilli-heads' getting together to find even more inventive ways of growing, eating and worshipping these culinary sticks of dynamite.

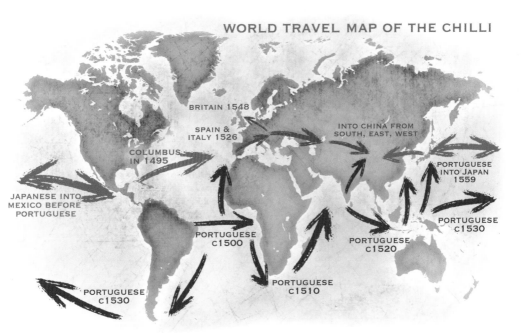

WORLD TRAVEL MAP OF THE CHILLI

BRITAIN 1548

SPAIN & ITALY 1526

INTO CHINA FROM SOUTH, EAST, WEST

COLUMBUS IN 1495

PORTUGUESE INTO JAPAN 1559

JAPANESE INTO MEXICO BEFORE PORTUGUESE

PORTUGUESE c1530

PORTUGUESE c1500

PORTUGUESE c1520

PORTUGUESE c1530

PORTUGUESE c1510

Bolivian Rainbow Chilli

Chinese White

CHILLI FACTS

World's Oldest Condiment

There is evidence that chillies were being eaten in Central and South America as long ago as 7,500 BC, making them the world's oldest condiment as well as its most ubiquitous today.

Tiny, round chillies were used as one of the earliest tax payments, paid to Aztec Emperors. The little, round Chiltepin still grows wild around the region on large plants that can live for years.

Capsaicin

Capsaicin is the active irritant in chillies that causes the burning sensation in mammals. The sensation has no lasting effect and in actual fact does no direct harm to cells. It tricks our central nervous system into releasing endorphins which produces a pleasurable sensation in the body. That's why eating spicy food can be so pleasurable. Although causing no direct harm, seriously hot chillies give the system a bit of a shock! A number of people having been hospitalised from messing with the superhots and capsaicin extracts.

Scoville Heat Units

Wilbur Scoville developed a method for measuring the heat of chillies in 1902, which involved tasting diluted pods and giving them a value. Bell peppers with no heat rate at zero and the world's hottest chillies rate at around 1.5 million SHU. That means one part chilli is still detectable when diluted with 1.5 million parts water.

Today, Scoville ratings are measured by High Performance Liquid Chromatography (HPLC), which separates out compounds so that capsaicin can be measured accurately.

Chilli Queen

25 year old Anandita Tamuly of Assam holds the record for eating superhot chillies, consuming a mouth-blistering 60 Bhut Jolokia in two minutes!

At the time, Bhut Jolokia was on record as the world's hottest chilli, nearly doubling the heat of its predecessor, the Red Savina. While the record for the hottest chilli gets broken again and again, Anandita's record still holds. It will be hard to beat!

Superfood

It is said that chillies can help fight off winter colds and eating them certainly helps lift the spirits. They are packed with vitamins, containing more Vitamin C than oranges, more Vitamin A than carrots and such high levels of Vitamin D that some athletes eat them prior to training to reduce the risk of injury.

The active ingredient in chillies, capsaicin, can reduce the amount of insulin needed to lower blood sugar levels after a meal by up to about 60%, which could be of benefit to diabetics and the obese.

Chillies are natural antioxidants and it has long been noted that cultures that regularly consume them have lower rates of stomach cancer. Recent tests on rats with prostate cancer showed that large doses of capsaicin caused the death of a high percentage of cancer cells, making it a possible part of a future cure.

BURN, BABY, BURN!

Be careful when trying new chillies. The burning sensation of some, like the Chiltepin, is quick, explosive and subsides very quickly but the heat of others, like the Habanero, builds slowly. Drinking water will not relieve the burning sensation of chillies. Some say drinking milk or eating yoghurt is the best method, others claim alcoholic drinks are the best way to dissipate capsaicin oil.

▶ Pest Control Savannah Style

Capsaicin has long been used as a pest control by chilli plants themselves, deterring mammals from eating them but having no effect on the nervous system of birds.

In parts of Africa and India, farmers plant a barrier crop of chillies or smear fences with them to keep elephants from their crops. A handful of dried chilli mixed in with your birdseed will deter those pesky squirrels, leaving your garden birds to happily munch away.

▶ Hell's Brimstone

19th Century priests in the USA condemned Chilli Con Carne, warning their flocks that the 'Soup of the Devil' was 'Hot as Hell's Brimstone'.

It was widely held that chillies were an aphrodisiac. This declaration ironically probably contributed to the popularity of chilli as a dish.

Legend has it that the outlaw Jesse James was so fond of a bowl of chilli that he refused to hold up the bank in McKinney, Texas because it was the town of his favourite chilli bar!

He wasn't prepared to be run out of that town for any amount of money!

World's Biggest Chilli

The Big Jim chilli from New Mexico is in the Guinness Book of Records for producing the largest pods, frequently over 30cm in length; quite impressive for a 60cm tall plant! The chillies are easy to grow, hot, tasty and great for stuffing.

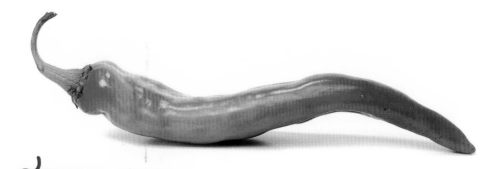

World's Largest Curry

The world's largest curry was cooked up by 60 Indian chefs in Delhi in June 2008; a 13 tonne Biryani including 85kg of chillies and 3,000kg of rice that needed three cranes to help lift all the ingredients. The reason for making such a large curry was unclear, especially since there was no prior record, but it didn't go to waste,being distributed amongst all the orphanages in the city.

▶ Hottest Part of a Chilli

Contrary to popular opinion, it is not the seeds that are the hottest part of a chilli, but the white placenta that surrounds them and runs in thick veins through the pod. Red chillies are 2-3 times hotter than green fruit, and dried pods are 2-10 times hotter than fresh.

[FAMOUS FIVE]

▶ There are five separate species of chilli;

Capsicum chinense
is the hottest species, including Habaneros and the Superhots.

....

▶ Most of the world's chillies belong to this species.

Capsicum annum, meaning annual, even though most are half-hardy perennials.

....

Capsicum frutescens, meaning 'shrubby', including Tabasco and Birdseyes.

....

Capsicum baccatum, meaning 'berry-like', including the Ajis, they tend to grow on large, vine-like plants.

....

Capsicum pubescens, meaning 'hairy', including South American Rocotos with their black seeds.

....

Anatomy of a Chilli ▶

There are numerous distinct parts to a chilli pepper, each with their own proper name. Dissect any chilli and you will find each of these parts.

The Pedical, or stalk holds the chilli pod onto the plant.

The Calyx joins the pod and stem.

Capsaicin Glands produce the chilli's heat.

Placenta holds the Capsaicin Glands.

The **Exocarp**, **Mesocarp** & **Endocarp** are the outer, mid-pod and inner flesh.

The Apex is the very tip of the pod.

The Seeds are the raison d'etre of the whole plant.

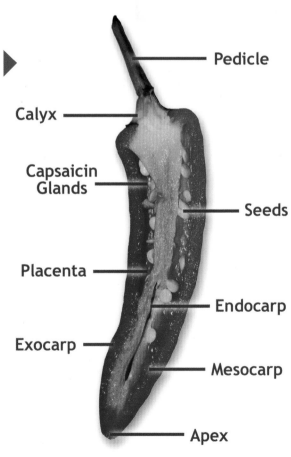

Pedicle

Calyx

Capsaicin Glands

Seeds

Placenta

Endocarp

Exocarp

Mesocarp

Apex

Krakatoa

Purple Jalapeno

HOW TO GROW CHILLIES

Get Ready to Plant

The best time of year to start planting chilli seeds in the UK is January to early March, for long season chinense varieties and February to April for shorter season annum, frutescen and other species. This is essential if you want your chillies to ripen by the end of the season.

Preparing Seeds

Germinating chilli seeds is quite easy, so if you follow these instructions carefully, you should have a good rate of success. Soaking your chilli seeds overnight in warm water will increase your germination rate. If you want to keep the water warm, soak seeds in gripseal bags and pop them into a thermos of warm water (30-40ºC) overnight.

▶ PLANTING SEEDS

The easiest and most effective method of planting is to use pre-formed Jiffy pellets. Use the Coir variety, not the compost.

Soak them until they have swollen to size and put two seeds into the hole at the top of each pellet, just below the surface. Gently squeeze the pellet to cover the seed. Remove the weaker seedling later on.

If you are planting into pots, you need to use a very free-draining compost mix. Peat is fairly disasterous for chillies as it is holds too much water, leaving roots cold and waterlogged.

A good mix is a 50/50 blend of coir and compost with a generous handful of vermiculite. The compost will provide all the necessary nutrients for young plants.

Coir, or processed coconut husk, is very effective at absorbing excess moisture and releasing it back as the plants need it. Vermiculite behaves in a similar way but is better at releasing nutrients back.

Fill one pot per seed-type to about 2cm below the rim, firm down the compost and soak thoroughly. Pop the seeds on top and cover with a fine layer of compost.

▶ Propagating Chilli Seeds

For best results, place in a heated propagator or a seed tray with clear lid in a warm place. Around 25-30°C is an ideal temperature and this will significantly increase germination. You will also get much faster results and the best chance of healthy seedlings. In a heated environment, you should start to see some action in 7-10 days.

Germination can be erratic, especially with chinese varieties and you may see seedlings emerging for several weeks. If you have planted into pots, try not to disturb the compost until you are quite sure all your seedlings have emerged.

Seedlings

When the seedlings start to appear, introduce some ventilation to your propagator or seed tray. Be careful not to let the temperature drop too much at night, as plants are very vulnerable to the cold at this stage.

Keep the compost moist but not wet. Overwatering is the biggest cause of chilli plant problems and at this early stage it can quickly encourage damping off.

The seed contains enough energy for the seedling to grow and produce its first set of true leaves, so there is no need to feed at this stage, although some growers use a 1/4 strength seaweed feed.

Growing on from Plug Plant Size

Four to six weeks after germination, plants should have produced two sets of true leaves and can be potted on carefully.

Avoid too much disturbance to the roots. If you have used coir pellets, this will not be a problem. Plant into 9cm pots, using a free-draining compost. Again, a 50/50 mix of coir and compost is ideal. Chilli plants do well in warm, sunny places, so a heated greenhouse, conservatory or sunny windowsill is ideal. Keep a close eye on your young plants, keeping compost moist. Feed them weekly with a seaweed or dedicated pepper feed.

Growing on from Plant Size

After another 4-6 weeks, plants will be outgrowing their pots and ready for their final positions. Roots will have filled the pot. Again, using a free draining compost/coir mix, carefully pot on into pots of a minimum 7 litre size. Chinense plants in particular will grow much larger in bigger pots so if you have the space, go up to a large bucket-size pot of 11-20 litres.

By this stage, an unheated greenhouse should suffice. This is obviously weather dependent. Chillies don't like the cold and shouldn't be left unprotected if temperatures fall much below 10°C. Temperateuresbelow 5°C will kill your plants.

In the summer months, hardier annuum chillies can be placed outside in a sheltered spot or on a warm patio. Acclimatize them slowly, bringing them in at night for the first week or whenever the temperature threatens to drop. Chinense varieties prefer really need a greenhouse.

Where necessary, use a cane to support the plants as they grow. Carry on feeding chillies with a dedicated chilli feed or seaweed extract at the suggested rate. A weekly foliar spray of Epsom Salts (Magnesium Sulphate) will encourgage leafy growth. Keep the compost moist, plants well spaced and make sure there is some ventilation.

Keep a careful check of any pests in the greenhouse, as they are better dealt with before an infestation starts. Check the underside of leaves and the top of the soil. Yellow sticky fly traps are very cheap and can help keep a track of any pests around. Note any yellow or mishapen leaves and check the defficiency guide for what this indicates.

Flowering and Fruit

Your chilli plants will produce pods on each of their side-stems so the more sidestems you have, the more fruit your plant will produce.

The flowers are insect-pollinated but that failing, they will self-pollinate, so a gentle shake of flowers will help ensure that they set. Once your plants start to flower, switch to a high potassium feed such as a half-strength tomato feed or dedicated chilli feed.

If you want a bumper crop of pods, feed as above. Heat-stressed plants will produce a smaller crop of hotter pods. Feed at half the suggested rate and let your plants almost dry out, watering them a little as they start to wilt.

If watching plants grow from seed to bear flowers and fruit does not get you hooked on chillies, the heat and flavour of your own fresh pods is sure to. When used stright off the plant, their flavour is fresher, fruiter and more intense.

Happy growing and bon appetit. Don't eat them all at once now!

REGIONAL CHILLIES

These chillies are used in cuisines around the world and are all seriously hot. They all have their distinct flavours and usages. Also see the Fire Chillies section to find out about the superhots.

▶ World's Hottest Chillies

HABANEROS

ORIGINATE
Although Habanero literally means 'from Havana', most traditional Habs come from Yucatan, Costa Rica & Belize. There are also variants of this chilli grown all across the world.

CHILLIES
Medium-sized, heart-shaped chillies, 4-5cm long, in a variety of colours. Habaneros have a light, fruity flavour with a searing heat that builds and builds. A wide variety of uses include sauces, salsas, Jerk marinades, Caribbean cooking, jellies & spiced alcohol. 350,000-450,000 SHU.

TYPES
Many types including Orange, Red, smoky-flavoured Chocolate, extra hot Red Savina, Paper Lanterns, crumpled yellow Fatalii, irregular-podded Malaysian Goronong, little Peruvian Whites, Big Sun, Mustard, Tobago Seasoning, Tasmanian, Apricot, Peach, Lemon & mild Suave.

SCOTCH BONNETS

BIRDSEYES

ORIGINATE
From the Caribbean, the name refers only to their likeness to traditional Scottish hats.

CHILLIES
Irregular, wrinkled pods of various shapes, sizes and colours. Bonnets are one of the most versatile of chillies with their distinctive hot, fresh and fruity flavour. Main uses are Caribbean cooking, Jerk dishes, chilli, soups and chicken dishes. 325,000SHU.

TYPES
Various colours including red, orange and yellow. Other varieties include Jamaican Hot Pepper & Caribbean Antillias.

ORIGINATE
Birdseye chillies have more variants around the world than any other chilli. A firm favourite across southern Africa, Thailand & India. 100-225,000 SHU.

CHILLIES
Short, narrow fruits tapering to a blunt point that sit proud on the plant. They dry well, pickle well and freeze well and impart a hot, light flavour into food. Versatile chilli used in many dishes around the world. They are domesticated plants that also grow wild.

TYPES
Numerous varieties such as African Devil or Piri Piri, Thai and Indian Hot Peppers.

CHILTEPIN

ORIGINATE
Known as the Mother of Chillies, this is the oldest-known variety and it still grows wild in the deserts of Arizona and Mexico. Archaeologists have proven that people were eating these chillies up to 7,500 years ago. The name Chiltepin comes from the Navaho Indian for 'flea chilli'. 100,000 SHU

CHILLIES
Part of the Birdseye group, Chiltepins are the size and shape of a large pea and have an explosive heat that subsides quickly. Main uses are soups, stews & sausages.

TYPES
Amarillo, Texas & Tarahumara.

ROCOTOS

ORIGINATE
Peru & Central America.

CHILLIES
Large and extremely pungent chillies, with distinctive black seeds. In Peru, these chillies are also known as Manzano, meaning apple, named for their resemblence to the fruit. Quite cold tolerant plants once germinated. Main uses are stuffing, salsas and sauces. The most common dish is Rocoto Rellenos, a kind of stuffed chilli dish.

TYPES
The most famous variety is the Rocoto Rojo, or Red, from the Peruvian Andes. Others include Brown, Yellow and Orange, the Aji from Equador & de Seda from Mexico. 225,000 to 350,000 SHU. Rocotos are of the pubescen species which will not cross with any other Capsicums.

▶ Ornamentals

Bred for the gardener as well as the chef, these chillies are the best of both worlds.

Some of the best Hot Ornamentals include:

Prairie Fire: Tiny plant suited to windowsills with a profusion of tiny leaves &colourful pods.	**Etna:** Award of Garden Merit for this patio-sized volcano with explosions of beautiful and seriously hot pods.	**Aurora:** Spectacular purple-tinged plant with hundreds of chillies in red, purple and orange.	**Topaz:** Compact Korean plant with emerald green pendant fruits ripening to an attractive gold.

Numex Twilight

Paper Lantern

Plant: A stunning ornamental chilli with bushy, dark green foliage that contrasts beautifully with multi-coloured fruits. Twilight grows to 45cm so is well suited to pot growth on a sunny patio.

Chillies: A profusion of purple flowers give way to 2cm long, tapered fruits which start out purple, turning to cream, yellow, orange and red as they ripen; all colours on the plant at once. Chillies are pretty spicy too.

Scoville Heat Units: 30,000 - 40,000

Plant: A chinense-type chilli with big fleshy leaves. Needs a little extra care and warmth so grows best in a greenhouse or conservatory in the UK. Chinense varieties have a long growing season.

Chillies: One of the most attractive Habanero chillies with red crumpled pods that resemble the shape of a Chinese paper lantern. Looks very attractive in a pot and has the advantage of producing extremely hot pods, even for a Habanero.

Scoville Heat Units: 450,000

Fillius Blue

Plant: Attractive, ornamental chilli with purple-tinged foliage that is sometimes speckled with white. The plants grow to around 60cm tall in a pot and have a short growing season. Award of Garden Merit (AGM).

Chillies: Small ovoid chillies start out a purple-blue colour, which they remain for a long time before maturing to red. Pick when blue if you want your chillies hot, as they actually become milder when they ripen.

Scoville Heat Units: 20,000 - 30,000

Explosive Blast

Plant: A stunning dwarf plant with bright green, bushy foliage and covered with tiny, bright flowers and pods.

Chillies: Gorgeous blunt little cones that mature from yellow to orange and red. Chillies are produced prolifically in clusters, over a long period of time. The pretty fruits glow in the sunlight. They are extremely pungent too, making a good addition to any meal, if you can bear to remove them from your plant!

Scoville Heat Units: 40,000

Bolivian Rainbow

Plant: Stunning ornamental plant from Bolivia. These chillies are extremely easy to grow and will start flowering and fruiting when they are very small. Plants will grow quite large or use a small pot to restrict growth.

Chillies: Small ovoid chillies start out a regal purple-before maturing through orange and yellow to red. All colours appear on the plant at once in a spectacular display. A firm favourite with gardeners.

Scoville Heat Units: 20,000 - 30,000

Chilly Chilli

Les Palco Hybrid

EXTREME CHILLIES

These are the superhots, all measuring in excess of a million Scoville Units. They all compete to be the world's hottest chilli but that title is constantly changing hands as new cultivars are found or bred!

▶ Naga Morich & Bhut Jolokia

ORIGINATE
Bangladesh (Naga),
Assam (Bhut)

TYPES
Bhut Jolokia in Red, Yellow, Chocolate, White and Peach. Naga Morich in Red & Black, extra large King Naga or Naga Mirch.

CHILLIES
These chillies are very close cousins, with little to tell them apart. Nagas are slightly smaller and more pimpled than one time world's hottest chilli, the Bhut.

Both have Scoville ratings of over a million. Pods are tri-lobed wedges and now come in a variety of colours, all seriously hot. Their fresh citrusy flavour is often over-looked in view of their incredible heat. Uses include Bengali dishes, chilli rubs, pickles, super-hot chilli sauces & oils.

▶ Trinidad Scorpion & Variants

ORIGINATE
Trinidad

TYPES
Trinidad Scorpion, Red, smooth little Yellow, extra hot Butch T, Jays Ghost Scorpion & Jays Peach Ghost Scorpion.

CHILLIES
From its Habanero-shaped top to the kick of its scorpion tail, this chilli means business. Originating in Trinidad, the chilli has a fruity flavour, coupled with a tremen-dous heat that has reached around 1.5 million SHU!

Butch T, a type of Scorpion bred by American hot sauce manufacturer Butch Taylor, held the Guinness title of World's Hottest Chilli for nearly two years before being toppled by the Carolina Reaper.

▶ Seven Pots & Variants

ORIGINATE
Chaguanas region of
Trinidad

TYPES
Red hot Red Seven Pot, pineapple-flavoured Yellow, Chocolate Douglah, the giant podded Jonah, Barrakapore, Primo.

CHILLIES
The Seven Pot get its name because it reputedly has enough heat to spice up a whole week of stews. Large, rounded, crumpled pods certainly reach heats of well over a million SHU. Numerous variants have emerged from the backwaters of Trinidad and more may yet be found. They are all seriously hot chillies reaching over a million SHU.

▶ Moruga Scorpion & Variants

ORIGINATE
Moruga, Trinidad

TYPES
Moruga Scorpion, Moruga Brainstrain.

CHILLIES
Large golfball size pods of incredible heat. Believed to be a Moruga/Scorpion hybrid, this chilli exceeds both in heat. The Moruga Scorpion was the first chilli to ever test more than 2 million Scoville Units, by the Chilli Pepper Institute in 2012. Relatively easy to grow, producing large numbers of pimpled round pods.

▶ Carolina Reaper

ORIGINATE
Carolina, USA

TYPES
Carolina Reaper

CHILLIES
The Reaper took the Guinness Title of World's Hottest Chilli in December 2013. Bred by Ed Currie of the Puckerbutt Pepper Company, it is reputedly a cross between a Pakastani Naga and a Red Habanero from the Caribbean island of St Vincent. The chilli looks mean, resembling a Moruga, with the tail of a serious Scorpion and believe me, it bites! The chilli has tested highs of 2.2 million SHU with an average Scoville rating recorded in the Guinness Book of Records as 1,569,300SHU.

SOUTH AMERICAN CHILLIES

The home of chilli peppers, Central and South America has the world's most varied chilli culture, with a huge range of varieties.

▶ MEXICO

A long tradition of hot cuisine has led to many varieties being grown for specific purposes. As well as fresh pods, Mexicans use dried and smoked chillies, known as Chipotles, and mixed spiced chilli powders, known as Moles.

JALAPENO
One of the best-known chillies, the waxy bullet pods are fresh and flavoursome. Usually picked green, they are used fresh, pickled and smoke-dried.

POBLANO
A large, glossy, heart-shaped chilli that is mild, aromatic and good for roasting & stuffing. Known as Anchos when dried.

ANAHEIM
A tall, high-yielding plant with long, tapered chillies. Sweet and mild.

CHILLI DE ARBOL
The Tree Chilli, named for its size and woody stems. Often used for ristras as they retain their blood-red colour when dried.

PASILLA
Extra long, thin pods that are used fresh or dried. Literally means 'little raisin' because of their texture when dried.

SERRANO
Thick-fleshed bullet pods grow on hairy-leaved plants. Fine-flavoured pods are used raw in salsas.

▶ PERU

Like Mexico, Peru has a long history of chilli culture and hundred of varieties. Integral to Peruvian cuisine, chillies are served at every meal.

AJI AMARILLO
Literally translates as Yellow Chilli. Huge plants, up to 2m tall, with 30cm long yellow pods. Pungent and often used dried.

LEMON DROP
The 'Kellu Ucha' is a popular Aji, hot, citrusy chilli with crumpled yellow pods.

Aji Panca
A dark Peruvian chilli, the name translates as 'red chilli'. A strong flavour that is popular in Peruvian cuisine.

ROCOTOS
A variety of hot, hairy-leaved plants with large ovoid chillies & black seeds. Serious hot, distinctive pods.

PERUVIAN PURPLE
Ornamental Pequin pepper with little clusters of mild, purple cone-shaped chillies.

▶ OTHER

There are a huge variety of chillies from all across Central & South America including Brazil, Bolivia, Equador, Costa Rica & Belize.

CAYENNE
Named after the capital of French Guiana, there are hundreds of varieties worldwide. Distinctive flavour and classic chilli shape.

BOLIVIAN RAINBOW
Much-acclaimed hot, ornamental variety covered with hundreds of tiny multi-coloured pods.

MALAGUETA
A chilli that crops up in the state of Bahia, in Brazil and also in Mozambique and Portugal. The chilli traversed the globe with Portuguese explorers.

POBLANO
A large, glossy, heart-shaped chilli that is mild, aromatic and good for roasting & stuffing. Known as Anchos when dried.

ANAHEIM
A tall, high-yielding plant with long, tapered chillies. Sweet and mild.

ASIAN CHILLIES

Although chillies were not introduced to Asia until the 1500s, they have come to dominate the cuisine of the continent. There are hundreds of varieties from all over Asia.

CHINA

Chinese chillies are not well documented but the west is beginning to learn about more of the many varieties in China.

SZECHUAN	FACING HEAVEN	CHINESE WHITE	SHABU SHABU
Long, thin-walled Cayenne type chilli that is very popular in Chinese cooking.	Hundreds of pretty and flavoursome conical chillies point skywards.	Flavoursome and hot, these chillies are also easy to grow. The pods are mostly used dried.	A superhot variant of Naga Jolokia, found growing along the border with Myanmar.

THAILAND

Hot, light and aromatic, Thai cuisine would be lost without chillies. Bird-eyes are the most common, others include:

PRIK KEE NOO	SUPERHOT THAI DEMON	THAI SUN	THAI DRAGON
Literally translates as the "Mouse Poo Chilli". Small but deadly.	A new hybrid producing many uniform, 7cm long red pods. Very hot.	30cm tall pot plant, with hundreds of tiny upward-facing fruits. Often grown ornamentally.	Small, pointed and fiery chillies are produced very early. Popular in the west.

INDIA

India today is the world's largest exporter of chillies and it is impossible to conceive of its cuisine without them. There are many different varieties grown across India but some of the more popular include:

ACHAR		KASHMIRI	
One of India's most popular culinary chillies, with a mild but distinctive flavour.		Mild pods with a distinctive flavour and blood-red colour. They are for the most part used dried in cooking.	
BANGALORE TORPEDO	**PUSA JWALA**	**FIRE CRACKER**	**RAJA'S PRIDE**
A classic East Indian chilli with long, thin pendant fruits.	Also known as the Finger Pepper, this hot variety is very popular.	Long, thin Indian hot pepper that crops very heavily and dries well.	A long, red & mild Cayenne type pepper.

OTHER

Hundreds of chillies from across Asia include:

VIETNAMESE TEARJERKER	HY HOT	YUTSAFUSA
Medium hot creased pods that grow upright. Thai-like in flavour.	High-yielding, pretty Cayenne from Hong Kong with straight, thick-fleshed fruits.	Many branches bear clusters of hot, deep red pods on this Japanese favourite.

USA CHILLIES

The world's oldest chillies still grow wild in the deserts of the southern States. The USA also produces many new cultivars, so chillies both ancient and modern play a large role in the region's cuisine and horticulture:

TABASCO	DATIL	FRESNO	RING OF FIRE
Originates in Mexico but made famous by the Louisiana hot sauce. Very tall plants, covered with little upright pods.	Golden wedge chillies from St Augustine, Florida. Hot as Habaneros with a Naga-like appearance.	Jalapeno-type chillies borne on short, bushy plants, good for pot growth. The Supreme version is a prolific fruiter.	Small, slender and extra hot Cayenne-type chillies on small plants. Prolific and usually the first to fruit in the UK.

FISH	SANTA FE GRANDE	BIG JIM	PETER PEPPER
Ornamental, hot Heirloom chilli with variegated pods. Used with fish.	Prolific producer of 10cm cone chillies with a fine flavour. Very popular plant & fruits.	Huge 30cm pods produced on small plants. Good for stuffing and does well in pots.	The world's most pornographic chilli, this novelty chilli has distinctive penis-shaped pods!

CARIBBEAN CHILLIES

The Caribbean is home to some of the world's hottest chillies, mostly from the Habanero and Scotch Bonnet family. Also check out the World's Hottest and Extreme Chillies sections. Popular Caribbean varieties include:

MORUGA	HABANERO CARIBBEAN RED	JAMAICAN HOT CHOCOLATE
Not to be confused with the superhot Moruga Scorpion, this is a smooth rounded chilli with the heat of a Habanero.	Ferociously hot Habanero that reaches 450,000SHU. Fruity flavoured pods grow on large plants.	Hot, strong and smoky, deep chocolate Habanero. A real connoisseur's chilli in rich chocolate colour.
BILLY GOAT	**KITCHEN PEPPER**	**ANTILLIAS CARIBBEAN**
Large, ovoid pods with a fresh, fruity flavour borne on pretty purple-stemmed plants.	Hot, flavoursome, pencil pods born on scrubby plants.	Hot Scotch Bonnet-type with strong aroma. Good for sauces.
JAMAICAN HOT RED	**BONNEY**	**ROCOTILLO**
Crumpled rotund chillies that are as dramatic-looking as they are hot.	Most popular chilli in Barbados, used exclusively for their hot mustard sauces.	Small, mild bell-pepper shaped chillies.

EUROPEAN CHILLIES

Some countries have a strong chilli culture and their popularity grows across Europe.

EASTERN EUROPE

Eastern Europe's chillies come mostly from Hungary, Bulgaria and Romania:

PAPRIKA
Medium hot chillies with very distinctive flavour, usually powdered.

HUNGARIAN WAX
Prolific and easy to grow Wax, or Banana. Mild and tasty. Hot Wax variants too.

BULGARIAN CARROT
Pretty, prolific heirloom variety with carrot-like pods. Known locally as Shipkas.

CHEESE CHILLIES
Large, ruffled, round, mild stuffing chillies, mostly from Hungary.

SOUTHERN EUROPE

More traditional pimientos come from Spain, mild chillies from Greece and there are numerous new Italian cultivars.

PEPPERONICI
Mild, sweet chillies from Italy and Greece, often used pickled.

SATAN'S KISS
A small Italian cherry-type that loses some of its heat when cooked.

PIMIENTOS
Numerous varieties of brightly-coloured chillies; mild, sweet & strung in ristras.

PIMIENTO DE PADRON
The Russian Roulette of tapas as only one in five pods are hot.

UK BRED

Chillies and gardening are both very popular in the UK and as a result, there are quite a number of chillies being bred here.

Naga Viper

DORSET NAGA
Seriously hot Naga variety that was once a contender for World's Hottest Chilli. This chilli has eventually found its place in the record books with the highest number of pods on one plant, a whopping 2,407!

INFINITY CHILLI
Bred by Nick Woods in the tropics of Grantham in Linconshire, the chilli briefly made it into the record books with a heat rating of 1,067,286 SHU

NAGA VIPER
Another brief entry into the Guinness Book of Records, the Naga Viper is a Naga hybrid, bred by Gerald Fowler in the Lake District reaching a record high for 2011 of 1,382,118SHU.

Fatalii

AFRICAN CHILLIES

Although not as widespread as in South America and Asia, chillies play a big part in some African cuisine and there are many varieties. Popular chillies include:

▶ East Africa

The area produces most of Africa's chilli exports.

African Snub:
A Kenyan chilli that is almost indistinguishable from the Mexican Jalapeno. Fresh, light and flavoursome with medium pungency.

Habanero Big Sun:
One of Africa's Habaneros. Large, slightly milder than other Habaneros with a strong fruity flavour.

Fatalii:
An extra hot Habanero from the Central African Republic. The original chilli is a gorgeous yellow colour although there are now variants of other shades.

▶ Southern Africa

This area has more chillies than any other in Africa and a strong chilli culture.

African Devil:
Also known as PiriPiri, short red fruits of incredible heat from Mozambique & South Africa but grows feral across Africa.

Zimbabwe Bird:
Seriously hot litte Pequin chillies cover bushes in prolific numbers. One of a large number of Bird chillies.

Pepperdew:
Mildly hot, sweet, round chillies from South Africa. A popular pickled variety.

STORY OF THE WORLD'S HOTTEST CHILLIES

It's not by accident that the world's hottest chillies come from the poorest areas of the globe. One of the effects of capsaicin on the body is the release of endorphins, so chillies have long been added to make bland food pleasurable.

In a few areas of the world, chilli plants have been selectively bred over the generations to produce pods of extreme heat, none more so than northern Asia and the Caribbean.

Chillies that fit into the category are Naga Jolokia variants from India, Bangladesh, China and Myanmar and pods from Trinidad; Seven Pots, Morugas and Scorpions and their variants.

Originally, the driving force behind this quest for the world's hottest chilli was primarily for practical purposes. If you were preparing large quantities of food, it made so much more sense to buy just one chilli pod that was hotter than the regular variety.

The Seven Pot, a Trinidadian chilli, is infamous for the ability of a single pod to give enough heat and flavour for a whole week of meals.

Tested at 577,000 Scoville Heat Units, the Red Savina, a type of Habanero chilli, sprung to fame in the Guinness Book of Records as the World's Hottest Chilli in 1994, marking the beginning of the Hot Competition. The pod was 115 times hotter than a Jalapeno, which is around 5,000SHU. More recent testing has been unable to duplicate this result and shows the Red Savina to be more in the region of 300,000 SHU, the heat of a standard Scotch Bonnet chilli.

The Red Savina held the Guinness title of World's Hottest Chilli for over three years. During this period the internet was becoming widely available to growers and Chilli Heads of the western world, who for the first time had easy access to the latest hot information. The fascination with superhots soared and the race was hotting up!

In 2007, a new chilli came onto the scene, the Bhut Jolokia, or Ghost Chilli, with a Scoville record of 1,001,304 SHU. The Ghost Chilli is a hybrid that occurs naturally in the Assam region in North India. There was a general amazement in the community of chilli heads

at the million Scoville barrier being smashed. The Bhut Jolokia is still a firm favourite of Chilli Heads, prized for its distinctive citrus flavour as well as its insane heat.

There were several contenders the throne of the Bhut including the Naga Morich, a Bangladeshi cousin of the Bhut, which was tested by Warwick University to 1,598,227SHU. Guinness, however, never confirmed this figure.

Another chilli, selectively bred from a Naga Morich by Michael and Joy Michaud, also gained much notoriety but not the Guinness Crown. A single Dorset Naga plant has since made in into the Record Book for producing whopping 2407 pods, more than any other plant on record. Don't eat them all at once now!

Whilst the eyes of the world were turned to the east, a number of challengers were gathering force in the west. The long reign of the Bhut came to an end in a spectacular pod fight between several contenders in 2011. Within a twelve-month period, three different chillies would take the Guinness title of World's Hottest Chilli.

Serious Chilli Heads had long been aware that Trinidad had some hidden superhots; the Scorpion, with a deadly heat and a mean kick in its tail, the Seven Pot and the Moruga, with its golf ball-sized pods.

Trinidad Scorpion pods had tested well over a million Scoville units by independent sources and when it was time for a revision of the Guinness Book of Records, it was expected that the Scorpion would find a place. Enter the under-pod from another unexpected location; Grantham in Lincolnshire. The Infinity Pod, so called because the burn goes on and on. The chilli was bred by new victor, Nick Woods of Fire Foods, and reached 1,067,286 SHU.

The victory was to be extremely short-lived, lasting for less than two weeks in February 2011 when Gerald Fowler's Naga Viper knocked the Infinity from its throne with a Scoville rating of 1,382,118. Things were looking hot for British-bred chillies! Disappointment for the Brit pods was unfortunately quick on its heels and by March 2011 the Butch T Trinidad Scorpion had been tested at 1,463,700SHU. This chilli was a worldwide effort with seeds from a Trinidad Scorpion being selectively bred by American hot sauce manufacturer, Butch Taylor who sent seeds to an Australian grower, the Hippy Seed Company, who grew the hottest Scorpion yet known.

Whilst the big pod fight was playing out on the global chilli scene, the Chilli Pepper Institute of New Mexico University had been conducting a rigorous two-year trial of the superhots. Their aim was to clarify not only which were the hottest pods on earth, but also the consistency of production. The results were published in 2012.

They announced the first chilli to ever test at more than 2 million SHU, the Moruga Scorpion (2,009,231SHU). They also recorded a pod of a Seven Pot variant, the Douglah, at 1.8 million SHU and a Bhut Jolokia pod at 1,578,548. The Guinness Book of Records didn't confirm the figures. The chilli world held its collective breath wondering what was coming up next. Surely nothing could top the Moruga? There was much talk of a chilli being bred in the USA by Ed Currie of the Puckerbutt Pepper Company, known only by its test name HP22B, or Higher Power, Pot 22, Plant B.

By December 2013, it had been christened the Carolina Reaper and passed the rigorous tests required by the Guinness Book of Records to be crowned World's Hottest Chilli. The official Scoville Rating is 1,569,300, that's around 300 times hotter than a Jalapeno. Individual pods have tested at more like 2 million. Either way, it'll burn the roof of your mouth off!

The story will undoubtedly not end here. Already rumours abound of possible new champions, mostly Trinidadian hybrids, such as the Seven Pot Primo and Bubblegum. Around the world, there are many fanatical horticulturalists who dream of breeding the World's Hottest Pod, so watch this space!

Butch T Scorpion

Yellow Trinidad Scorpion

CHILLI PLANT PESTS, PROBLEMS & DISEASES

▶ Prevention is Better than cure

Everyone grower looks forward to a healthy crop of hot pods at the end of the season. A little care in advance can help ensure you are not disappointed. Prevention is easier than the cure with most chilli plant problems, diseases and pests. A little care and attention in advance of planting and through the growing cycle can save you a lot of time and stress.

▶ Eight Point Plan for Preventing Chilli Plant Problems

1. Get your growing medium right.
This should include all the correct nutrients for the growth of young plants, whilst having good drainage to avoid problems of excessive water. The ideal combination for pepper plants is a 50/50 mix of compost and coir, with a few generous handfuls of vermiculite thrown in.

2. Get watering right.
Soil should be moist but never overwet. Overwatering can cause major problems with nutrient deficiencies, specifically nitrogen deficiency. Overwet soil also encourages a variety of pests, fungal infections and diseases.

3. Get feeding right.
Make sure you feed your chilli plants correctly. Overfeeding can be as damaging as underfeeding, since excessive amounts of one nutrient can cause another to be locked out of the plant. Seedlings should be fed weekly with a half strength seaweed feed, or similar general plant food. After being potted into their 9cm pots, switch to full strength seaweed feed. Once flowering begins, a high potash or half strength tomato feed is suitable. There are also dedicated pepper feeds.

4. Get the temperature right.
Whilst chilli plants can survive higher and lower temperatures, they thrive between 15 and 30°C. Excessive heat or cold can cause problems with the uptake of different nutrients and cause problems of humidity, wet soil or pots drying out too frequently.

5. Get the humidity right.
Plants need to perspire in order to get good water flow through them, delivering nutrients to all parts of the plant. A damp greenhouse can also provide a breeding ground for fungal infections and moulds. Keep your greenhouse well ventilated, whilst keeping an eye on the temperature. Keep your plants well-spaced, as overcrowding can have a negative impact on ventilation as well as light levels.

6. Greenhouse Hygiene
Poorly maintained greenhouses can provide breeding grounds for diseases as well as plenty of hiding places for pests. Pots and

planters should be cleaned out at the end of each growing season to avoid the build up of pathogens. If you are growing directly into the soil, don't forget to rotate your crops.

Remove any dead plant material, which can provide hiding places for pests as well as attract moulds and fungi. Remove any diseased plants as soon as possible to avoid the spread of pests and diseases.

7. Be Vigilant
Regular checks of your greenhouse and plants will help you to discover any problems early on, making them easier to deal with. Hunt out larger pests such as slugs, snails and caterpillars regularly and check the underside of leaves and plant growing tips for signs of smaller pests. Sticky yellow fly papers hung in your greenhouse will help you to see what pests are around, as well as catching a good number of them.

8. Introduce the Good Guys
Nature's pest controls are far more effective than manmade chemicals. Ladybirds, Lacewings and some Parasitic Wasps are all effective predators. Encourage them into your greenhouse by leaving the doors open or relocate them if you can. If you have an infestation of pests, you can purchase a range of Biological Controls over the internet during the course of the growing season.

Providing the right growing conditions for your chilli plants will go a long way to preventing problems. If you do notice any irregularities, try to diagnose the problem quickly and act upon the solution. The next section will help you with this.

Leaf burn

CHILLI PLANT PESTS

▶ Aphids & Whitefly

Greenhouse Aphids and Whitefly are amongst the most destructive of greenhouse pests and they are now largely resistant to pesticides making them extremely hard to irradiate. Sprays only have an effect on flying insects and not their eggs or young. They breed in large numbers, feed on plant sap and introduce plant disease. An infestation of these critters can completely ruin your chances of a good crop of chillies. Keep a careful check on your plants and deal with any unwanted intruders quickly. They can be managed if not completely eradicated.

Aphids Treatment

Be vigilant and deal with as quickly as possible.
1. Gently wipe leaves with a damp cloth to remove as many larvae as possible.
2. A sprinkling of Derris dust or Diatomaceous Earth will help deter aphids.
3. These critters like greenhouse warmth so take your chilli plants outside for a few days, as long as there's no risk of frost.
4. Spray plants down with lightly pressured water from a hose, being careful not to damage plants.
5. There are a number of pesticide sprays that will help control populations but they won't eradicate the problem. Remember that pesticides also harm the good guys.
6. Encourage, or relocate, ladybirds into the greenhouse or you can purchase Aphidus (a parasitic wasp) and Aphidolites, both effective predators. This is the most effective way of banishing aphids.
7. Be vigilant and keep repeating your treatment.

Aphids Symptoms

1. Flying insects around plants and larvae at growing tips and underside of leaves.
2. Discoloured patches on leaves.
3. Discarded white egg-casings at the soil surface and on leaves.
4. Sticky residue on leaves, often with casings stuck to it.
5. The presence of ants, which farm aphids, placing them onto leaves so they can feed off larvae.
6. Twisted and distorted new growth.

◗ Red Spider **Mites**

These critters can be a big problem, particularly later in the season in the greenhouse. They are tiny and can be hard to spot, but in large numbers cause serious damage.

Red Spider Mites **Symptoms**

1. A fine, pale mottling to the upper side of leaves.
2. In infestations, a fine grey webbing on leaves.
3. Loss of leaf colour.
4. Tiny moving dots and eggs on underside of leaves. Tap onto white paper & check for tiny movement across it.

Red Spider Mites **Treatment**

1. They favour dry conditions, so lightly mist with water if conditions are dry.
2. There are a number of pesticides available, or "NiteNiteSpidermite' is an organic control.
4. Phytoseiulus is a natural predator of Spider Mites and can be bought online.

◗ Thrips

AKA Thunder Flies are tiny little winged insects around 2mm in length, ranging in colour from yellow to black, dependent on species. They damage plants by sucking the sap from leaves, buds and fruit and introducing infections.

Thrips **Symptoms**

1. Speckled appearance on leaves, which is actually hatching thrips, emerging from eggs buried into leaf tissue.
2. Distorted, misshapen developing leaves.
3. Bleached or browning spots or streaks on pods.
4. Silvery streaks on flower petals.
5. Browning patches on leaves.
6. Groups of adult thrips at veins on the underside of leaves.

Thrips **Treatment**

1. Spray plants with a soap solution, washing up liquid will work but horticultural soap is better.
2. There are a number of pesticides on the market or 'Pest Off' is an effective organic control.
3. Thrip predators include Amblyseius cumeis, which can be purchased online.

▶ Fungus Gnats

In small numbers, these critters do not do much harm but in the case of an infestation, larvae seriously damage plant root systems. Overwatering and under-ventilation both encourage Fungus Gnats.

Fungus Gnats Symptoms

1. Quite visible small black flies hovering aimlessly around the plants, particularly at the soil surface.
2. In infestations, edges of leaves become chlorotic, turning yellow & white because the plant cannot uptake enough water through damaged roots.
3. Stunted growth.

Fungus Gnats Treatment

1. Bottom water into a tray under your plant pot to let soil top dry out.
2. Sprinkle surface with Diatomaceous Earth, or Fossil Flour.
3. Yellow paper flytraps will catch surprisingly large numbers of adults.
4. 'Gnat Off' is an effective organic larvacide, added into plant feed until the infestation is eradicated.

▶ Slugs & Snails

These regular garden pests need no introduction. They can decimate chilli plants but are quite controllable if you are vigilant.

Slug & Snail Symptoms

1. Slime trails around the greenhouse.
2. Leaves munched around the outside.
3. Holes in pods.
4. The presence of slugs and snails!

Slug & Snail Treatment

1. Seek out and destroy regularly; salt baths, beer traps, slug pellets, porridge oats, the scissors of mercy... everyone has their favourite methods of dispatch!

▶ Pepper Maggots

These yellowish grubs feed on the inside of pods causing them to ripen prematurely and drop.

Pepper Maggots Symptoms

1. Pods dropping off plants at early stage.
2. Tiny maggot holes in pods

Pepper Maggots Treatment

Pick off the infected pods and destroy.

CHILLI PLANT DEFICIENCY GUIDE

IRON
New growth has patches of yellow/white between veins. Can spread across whole leaf.

CALCIUM
Mishapen new growth ; cupped, curled & crumpled. Old growth unaffected.

NITROGEN
Old growth affected first then moving up the plant Leaves turn yellow across the leaf from tip to stem.

POTASSIUM
Leaf edges turn yellow on younger growth. Yellow or dead patches may become pinholes.

MAGNESIUM
Old leaves turn yellow, from leaf tip inwards. Veins remain green.

MANGANESE
Older growth displays yellow spots and long interveinal holes

PHOSPHORUS
Old leaves turn dark green, sometimes purple Will move up the plant if unchecked.

CHILLI PLANT DEFICIENCIES

As with all plants, chillies need a range of nutrients and micronutrients to maintain healthy growth. When planted into pots, the only access to these nutrients a plant has is through you, so you need to make sure you keep a healthy balance. Although plants need these nutrients in tiny quantities, deficiencies can have some dramatic effects on plant health.

Plants can display a range of symptoms from chlorotic (yellowing) to necrotic (dying) leaves, dark or purple patches on leaves, twisted leaves and stems, stunted growth and root problems.

Iron deficiency

▶ Prevention of Defficiency Problems

As with all plant problems, the best way to deal with plant deficiencies is to keep vigilant to begin with and avoid the problems of nutrient inbalances.

1. Get the potting mix right. This should include all the correct nutrients for the growth of young plants whilst having good drainage to avoid problems of excessive water. A good combination for pepper plants is a 50/50 mix of compost and coir, with a few generous handfuls of vermiculite thrown in.

2. Get watering right. Soil should be moist but never overwet. Overwatering causes two major problems. The first is that it leaches nutrients out of the soil, leaving less available to the plant. The second is that waterlogged roots find it difficult to absorb nutrients.

3. Get feeding right. Make sure you are feeding your chilli plants at the correct dose. Overfeeding can be as damaging as underfeeding, since excessive amounts of one nutrient can cause another to be locked out of the plant. Do not assume that increasing the feed will solve deficiency problems, you might just make it worse. Take time to diagnose the problem properly before acting upon it.

4. Get the temperature right. Whilst chilli plants can survive higher and lower temperatures, they thrive between 15 and 30°C. Excessive heat or cold can cause problems with the uptake of different nutrients.

5. Get the humidity right. Plants need get good water flow through them in order to deliver nutrients to all parts of the plant. Too humid or too dry an environment can cause problems with deficiencies.

▶ Nutrient Mobility

When deficient in a nutrient, a plant will always try to move the element from older growth to sustain new growth. However, whilst some elements are quite mobile, others cannot be unlocked from old growth at all. Deficiency of mobile nutrients will always show up in older leaves whereas deficiency of non-mobile nutrients will be displayed in new growth.

Common mobile nutrients; nitrogen, magnesium, phosphorus.
Nutrients with intermediate mobility; potassium, sulphur, zinc, copper, manganese.
Non-mobile nutrients; iron, calcium, boron.

▶ Iron Deficiency

Iron plays an important function in the production of chlorophyll and enzymes. Deficiency causes stunted growth in chilli plants and is characterised by interveinal chlorosis, or the yellowing of leaves whilst leaf veins remain green. It affects the new growth.

Chlorotic patches appear first but these can grow to cover the whole leaf. In extreme cases, leaf tissue becomes completely white.

There is sufficient iron in most composts and soils for your plants needs. Iron deficiency is more commonly caused by a lock out of nutrients. With iron, this could be high soil ph, high temperatures or excessive phosphorus in feed. Check php, feed suitablility and adjust temperateure as necessary.

Iron deficiency can be treated with chelated iron, commonly available in garden centres. Foliar spray at half the recommended dose.

You will see the green start to flush back into leaves within a few days and, apart from any completely white patches, leaf tissue will completely recover. Be careful not to overfeed with iron as this can in turn lock out phosphorus.

▶ Calcium Deficiency

Calcium is important for cell division and its deficiency is characterised by distorted new growth and weakened stems. New leaves have a twisted, bubbled appearance and edges can become necrotic. Old growth is not affected, as calcium is the least mobile of elements. If calcium is deficient during fruiting, plants may develop Blossom End Rot, with sunken, necrotic patches developing at the blossom end of pods.

An application of CalMag (Calcium Magnesium feed) can help but it would be unusual for there not to be sufficient Calcium in garden compost. It is more commonly a problem of nutrient lockout. Excessive nitrogen and/or potassium hinders the plant's ability to take on calcium, so check you are not feeding excessively. Calcium deficiency can also be the result of low transpiration. If your pots are continually drying out, this could be contributing to the problem and you should alter your watering regime to keep soil more constantly moist.

Nitrogen deficiency

▶ Nitrogen Deficiency

Of all the elements, nitrogen plays the biggest role in plant growth. It is responsible for the production of chlorophyll and amino acids. Nitrogen deficiency can have a serious impact on the growth and general health of chilli plants. Nitrogen is the most mobile of elements so the lower leaves become yellow first, the deficiency working its way up the plant. In severe cases leaves can form brown patches or flush with purple and the plant may drop these leaves. Plant growth becomes completely stunted and it can take a long time for plants to recover. Affected leaves will not recover.

It is unlikely that nitrogen deficiency is caused by an actual absence of nitrogen, more likely the plant is unable to access it. The most common cause cause is overwatering. A film of water around roots makes it difficult to take on nitrogen. Do not try to add extra fertiliser, as excessive nitrogen will have the effect of locking out other elements, such as calcium. Let soil dry out and adjust watering. Foliar spray with a solution of Epsom Salts (Magnesium Sulphate) at a rate of 2 teaspoons per litre of water. This will aid the production of chlorophyll and speed up recovery.

▶ Magnesium Deficiency

Magnesium helps support healthy leaf tissue, in particular leaf veins. It aids photosynthesis and is needed in quite large quantities. Deficiency is characterised by the chlorosis of lower leaves, from the leaf tips moving inwards, sometimes just around the leaf margins. The affected areas can become pale yellow with leaf veins remaining green. Plant growth is stunted.

A foliar spraying of Magnesium Sulphate (Epsom Salts) at a solution of 2 teaspoons per litre is recommended. This is the fastest way to get magnesium into plants and also avoids the build up of salts that soil feeding can produce. Check your plant feed as magnesium lockout can be caused by excessive potassium, in which case Epsom Salts application may have little or no effect.

▶ Potassium Deficiency

Potassium plays a major role in plant health, helping to create sturdy stems, aiding photosynthesis and disease resistance. Potassium deficiency is characterised by scorched leaf tips and edges on the middle leaves of the plant, that can turn brown and die.

Older leaves may display a mottled pattern and stems become brittle.

Potassium deficiency can be caused by excessive perspiration of plants, so check the humidity in your greenhouse and mist with water if too dry. Potassium can also be displaced by excessive calcium or sodium so check your feed and soil. Poor quality coir, for example, can add salt to compost. A high potassium, or potash, feed such a a general tomato feed, should rebalance this deficiency.

▶ Phosphorus

Phosphorus is associated with the rigorous growth of the whole plant, in particular root growth and reproduction. Stunted, weak growth is evident when phosphorus is deficient. Older leaves become dark green, flushing to purple and plants will be unlikely to flower. Problems can extend across the whole plant if deficiency is severe.

Chilli plants find it difficult to take on phosphorus in low temperatures, or if the soil ph is too low. Excessive iron can also hamper the uptake of phosphorus, although this is unlikely unless you have been applying it. Use any fertiliser with a high ratio of phosphorus, like tomato feed or slower-acting bonemeal.

▶ Sulphur

Sulphur plays an important role in root growth and the supply of chlorophyll. Middle growth is affected first, becoming yellow fairly evenly across the whole leaf, including the veins. Often the chlorosis starts at the stem-side of the leaf, travelling outwards. If unchecked, the whole plant can become affected.

Excessive heat hampers the uptake of sulphur so check the temperature and ventilate as necessary. Foliar spray with Epsom Salts solution at a rate of 2 teaspoons per litre.

phospherus deficiency

MICRONUTRIENTS

▶ Manganese

Manganese is important for the actions of enzymes within plants, amongst other things. Deficiency is characterised by yellow spots in the young growth, which may become necrotic and/or form elongated holes. Foliar feed with a half strength solution of manganese sulphate, available at most garden centres. Garden manure added to pots also works well, but is much slower acting.

Boron

Boron is needed in tiny amounts but plays a role in seed production, cell division and keeping stems healthy. Boron deficiency displays at the growing tips first; sometimes these die off completely. Newer growths can curl upwards or become spotted like a strawberry. Stems become brittle, sometimes hollow. Secondary roots are swollen and short.

Check for signs of potassium deficiency as plants need potassium to absorb boron, so the two can often go hand in hand. To re-introduce boron to your plants, foliar spray with a solution of ¼ teaspoon Borax, or Boric Acid, into 1 litre water. Manure and bonemeal are also good ways of introducing boron, but much slower acting.

Copper

Copper is essential for healthy stems and new growth. Where deficient, plant growth will be stunted. Growing tips may die back completely and/or new growth wilts and may become chlorotic. Stems loose their strength and become bendy. Copper deficiency often goes hand in hand with nitrogen deficiency so check for signs of this. Foliar feed with a half strength solution of Copper Sulphate.

Zinc

Zinc is needed in small quantities and plays a minor role in a large number of processes in the plant. It is important in the production of chlorophyll, the absorption of water and the growth of leaf and stem. Plants that are zinc deficient will display yellow or grey patches between the veins of new growth. End leaves may form a rosette or appear narrow and distorted. Treat with a half strength foliar spray of Zinc Oxide or Chelated Zinc or some people even suggest burying a galvanized nail in the soil. Make sure you blunt the end first to avoid injuries.

CHILLI PLANTS PROBLEMS

Powdery Mildew

This disease affects chilli plant leaves, typically in the flowering and fruiting stage in the most humid part of the summer. It can severely affect your crop size. The disease looks exactly as its name suggests, like a powdery white mildew.

Symptoms

1. Patchy growth of white powdery substance that slowly covers the underside of leaves, occasionally on upper side too.
2. Yellow and brown patches on upper side of leaves, where mildew is present on underside.
3. Leaf edges may roll upwards to reveal white, powdery growth.
4. Leaf drop.

Treatment

1. Prevention is key with this pathogen. Make sure your plants are well spaced and ventilated so that they can dry out between waterings.
2. Chemical controls for Powdery Mildew are fungicides, the most effective of which is Myclobutanil. Organic gardeners use Sulphur and Potassium Bicarbonate.

▶ Edema

This is a condition caused by a chilli plant taking on more water through its root system that it can use in growth or transpire through its leaves. It causes strange-looking crystalline growths on leaves. In itself, it causes little harm but is symptomatic of other problems.

Symptoms

1. White crystalline growth particularly on the underside of leaves and along leaf veins.

Treatment

Check watering levels, soil should be moist but not wet. A more likely cause is poor ventilation, so that plants are growing in an over-humid environment. Increase ventilation.

▶ Flower Drop

This is quite a common problem, particularly early in the season. Especially with chinense varieties, you will find that the first flush of flowers either not set at all, or set only for the newly forming pod to drop with the flower. Usually, the problem just rectifies itself and the next flowers set. However, there are a few common causes of flower drop.

Symptoms

1. Pollination failure. Chilli flowers are both insect pollinated and self pollinating, so you can remedy this by giving flowers a gentle shake. Alternatively, brush gently from flower to flower with a soft kids paintbrush.

2. Overwatering is the most common cause of all chilli growing problems and can cause flower drop. Underwatering can also cause

flower drop. Keep soil moist but not wet. A generous helping of coir or vermiculite in the compost will soak up excess water and release it back as the plant needs it.

4. Unstable temperatures such as cold nighttime and high daytime ones. Stabilize temperature by insulating at night or ventilating better in the day.

Edema

▶ Blossom End Rot

This condition develops in green fruits of chillies, peppers and tomatoes. It a problem caused by calcium deficiency, caused either by a sudden increase in demand for calcium as the fruit develops or by excessive nitrogen, reducing the uptake of calcium. It is essential for plants to have a good flow of water. Plants is small pots are particularly susceptible to drying out and water logging, which can prevent the distribution of calcium around the plant.

Symptoms

1. Blossom End Rot starts with a small legion at the blossom end of the fruit that appears water soaked. It affects fruits that are quite well developed.
2. As the legion grows, it becomes sunken and turns colour to dark brown and in severe cases it can completely cover the lower half pod the fruit.

Treatment

1. Adjust watering to keep moisture levels more constant.
2. Check and adjust your plant feed, to avoid excessive nitrogen which promotes leafy growth, leaving less calcium for fruit.
3. Foliar application of calcium are recommended by some, but usually quite poor in rectifying fruit problem due to poor movement around the plant.
4. Foliar application of Magnesium Sulphate (Epsom Salts) can aid the uptake of calcium.
5. Remove affected fruits to prevent plant stress. You will not be able to save these.

▶ Leaf Burn

Patches of pale brown, almost papery leaf tissue on otherwise healthy leaves. Water, splashed onto leaves in the heat of the day, acts like a magnifying glass onto the leaf, concentrating the suns energy onto small areas of the leaf.

Symptoms

1. Light brown to white marks in splash formations or concentrated around the edges of leaves, particularly on lower leaves. The legions generally don't bleed into the leaf, the edges remain sharp and the surrounding area is unaffected.
2. Affected areas become paper thin, almost transparent. The leaf tissue is completely dead.

Treatment

The affected area will not recover but unless the burn is severe, the plant should not be too affected. Leaf burn can be avoided quite easily.

1. Water in the early morning or evening, out of the heat of the day.
2. Water slowly, taking care not to splash leaves, or let plants soak water up from a tray placed under the pot.

DRIED CHILLIES

Many people consider dried chillies to be a poor, store-cupboard substitute for fresh. This impression of them has probably been informed by using old and poorly crushed chillies that have lost their flavour.

In parts of the world with a highly developed chilli culture, dried versions are used alongside fresh for flavour as well as heat.

Chillies lose none of their heat during the drying process but do take on a sometimes very different flavour that can impart a rich, sweet or smoky flavour into food. Whole dried pods retain more of their flavour than crushed or powdered.

With a chilli culture that goes back thousands of years, the Mexicans have developed the most sophisticated range of dried and smoked chillies. As well as many varieties of whole pods, they use 'Moles', which are dried chilli blends based on the holy trinity of Ancho, Mulato and Pasilla.

Roasting or toasting the pods in an oven or frying pan prior to soaking will intensify the flavour of the chillies.

To roast, remove the seeds and stalks and spread out on a baking sheet in a medium heat oven for 4-5 minutes or toast them in a dry, heavy-based frying pan on a medium heat. Do not let them burn as this will completely

destroy the flavour. Dried chillies should be rehydrated before use to soften them and release their flavour.

Remove the stalks and seeds and submerge the pods in boiling water for 20 minutes until they have regained some of their original shape and colour. They are then ready to cut, puree or use whole.

Handle dried chillies with the utmost care as capsaicin oil will be left on your hands. Always store out of the reach of children.

Some of the more interesting dried chillies available are listed overleaf.

ANCHO

CHIPOTLE MECO

BHUT JOLOKIA

CHIPOTLE

HABANERO

PEQUIN

KASHMIRI

CHAKASANG

NEW MEXICO RED

CHILTEPIN

GUAJILLO

PASILLA

THAI BIRDSEYE

CASCABEL

CHILLI DE ARBOL

Alepo
Mild, crushed and salted chilli from Turkey.

Ancho
Literally meaning 'broad', these large Mexican chillies have a sweet, fruity flavour and a moderate heat. Often used for stuffing, soups and sauces.

Aji Amarillo
Beautiful orange pods from Peru with fruity flavour & intense heat.

Bhut Jolokia
Superhot pods even when fresh, their heat intensifies as they shrink during the drying process. Handle with extreme caution.

Birdseye
Small but deadly, these are a very useful store cupboard chilli. Most come from India and are the commonly found dried chilli.

Cascabel
Large, apple-shaped pods with rattling seeds. A moderate heat with a nutty flavour that compliments stews and soups.

Chile de Arbol
Meaning 'The Tree Chilli'. This long, thin chilli grows on large woody plants. Very hot pods that keep their rich red colour when dried.

Chipotle
Chipotles are smoked Jalapeno chillies that take on a rich, smoky flavour and a wonderful aroma. A distinctive flavour to enrich soups and sauces. There are a number of varieties of Chipotle including Morita & Meco.

Guajillo
A sweet, medium hot chilli with a distinctive tea-like flavour. Guajillos are very popular in north Mexico for salsas.

Habanero
A real connoisseur's chilli with a fruity flavour and a searing heat. One of the world's classic pods. Very versatile.

Kashmiri
Distinctive Cayenne-type with medium heat and robust flavour.

Mulato
One of the three Mexican Mole chillies, Mulatos have a rich flavour of dried fruit. They are usually used puréed.

Pasilla
Another of the Mole chillies, this is a favourite for its rich flavour. Pasilla literally means 'little raisin'.

Thai
There are two common varieties of Thai chillies; small Birdseye-type and larger, more aromatic pods.

PRESERVING CHILLIES

▶ Drying Chillies

Drying is a great way to preserve your leftover chillies and there are several ways to do it. Scotch Bonnets, Habaneros and other fleshy varieties tend not to dry very well, unless you have a dedicated dehydrator.

Drying is more suited to waxier chillies such as Birdseye and Indian Peppers. Traditionally, chillies would be laid out in the sun to dry, giving both warmth and ventilation, but this is not always possible in cooler climates.

The important thing to remember is to keep your chillies warm and dry. Around 25°C is optimum, much higher and you risk a very brittle product, lower and you risk losing your chillies to mould.

Rinse the chillies in salty water to kill off any surface bacteria and help prevent mould. Spread them out on some moisture-absorbent tissue in a warm place such as a greenhouse or airing cupboard, turning regularly until completely dried. Store in an airtight container or use a coffee grinder to grind them to powder.

Alternatively, string up your chillies in a Ristra, or long hanging chain of chillies. Ristras originate in Mexico and make lovely decorations or gifts, fresh or dried.

Wrap strong cotton around the stems of numerous chillies to tie in a long bunch, or thread through the stems with a needle and hang up in a warm, dry place to dry.

▶ Pickling Chillies

Pickling works well for most types of chilli, keeping them crisp and hot. Pack colourful chillies together to make pretty gifts.

Ingredients
0.5kg chillies
1 litre distilling vinegar (must have high acidity rate)
6 tbsps sugar
3 tbsps salt
5 bay leaves
15 peppercorns
Few slices lemon

Method
Remove any damaged chillies, make a couple of tiny slits into each remaining pod and wash thoroughly in salt water. Pack into pre-sterilised, wide-mouthed jars or bottles with the peppercorns, bay leaves and lemon slices, filling to 1cm below the rim.

Heat the salt and sugar in the vinegar until dissolved and the mixture is almost boiling. Pour into the jars to cover the chillies and seal. Store for at least 2 weeks before use.

▶ Freezing Chillies

Chillies freeze reasonably well, retaining most of their flavour and heat. Freezing is the best way to preserve fleshier chillies like Scotch Bonnets and Habaneros.

To freeze chillies whole, spread them out on a baking tray so they are not touching, freeze and pop into a sealed bag or container. This way they do not clump together.

Frozen chillies, however, do not always keep their shape or texture well so you may prefer to process them first.

Remove the stalks and the seeds if you like (they can go a bit brown on freezing) and freeze in a sealed bag. You can them smash the bag with a rolling pin and use as required.

Alternatively, pack chopped chillies into an ice cube tray to make easily measured portions. Store chilli cubes in a bag in the freezer.

CHILLIES & HEALTH

Looking for a way to fight infections, burn extra calories or lower your blood pressure? Several ongoing studies have shown that just adding hot peppers to your next meal could be a delicious way to ramp up your health.

Capsaicin is the colourless, odourless, flavourless phytochemical that makes chillies hot and it is also the magic ingredient that gives them a host of health benefits. The hotter the chilli, the higher the capsaicin content and the higher the antioxidant level.

Capsaicin is widely available as as a dietary supplement and medicinal aid, dried into a powder, concentrated into an oil and used in topical ointments and creams.   Or you can just eat a load of chillies!

Vitamins, Anti-Oxidants, Immune Boosting And General Health

Vitamin A: Chilli peppers are extremely rich in vitamin A, which is essential for maintaining healthy tissues of the respiratory, reproductive and gastrointestinal tracts.

Beta-carotene: Hot peppers are also an excellent source of beta-carotene, which converts to vitamin A in the body. The bright red colour of hot peppers is a testament to the presence of this carotenoid antioxidant, which helps reduce symptoms of arthritis and asthma.

Beta-cryptoxanthin: Chillies contain high concentrations of another carotenoid called beta-cryptoxanthin. There is plenty of scientific research supporting the belief that carotenoids have vast protective effects. In a recent clinical study, researchers found that dietary beta-cryptoxanthin was associated with a lower risk of arthritis.

Vitamin B-6: Chilli peppers are also rich in Vitamin B-6 or pyridoxine, which studies show helps the breakdown of protein in the body and plays a critical role in maintaining the health of red blood cells.

Vitamin C: In addition, hot peppers also have high vitamin C content.

Trace Elements: Other elements that can be found in capsaicin include vitamin K, which helps promote normal blood clotting, and manganese, which is an essential trace mineral.

Peppers As A Diet Aid

Can peppers really help with weight loss and do they act as a diet aid? Capsaicin has several different properties that promote weight loss. The high Capsaicin content in hot peppers makes them a powerful component in any weight loss diet. A study conducted in April 2010 and published in the "International Journal of Obesity" showed that capsaicin improves metabolism, increases the oxidation of fat and augments energy expenditure of energy, all of which encourage weight loss.
Capsaicin revs up your metabolism. Seasoning your food with hot peppers provides you with plenty of metabolism boosting capsaicin, which works two ways to encourage weight loss- firstly, spicy foods help you eat less

and feel more satisfied with your food and secondly, the metabolism boosting properties of the capsaicin help you burn fat faster. A recent study that was done revealed that hot peppers with a higher content of capsaicin can increase your metabolism by as much as 20% and those who ate hot chilli peppers on average about three times a day, burned more fat on a regular basis.

Chilli Peppers And Parkinson's Disease, Cancer & Diabetes

With ongoing research on chilli peppers and their potential effects on various health conditions, more and more health benefits continue to be discovered. While health benefits have been proven beyond any doubt, in some cases, studies show the potential benefits but more studies have yet to be done before it can be universally accepted. Still, there's no doubt that the use of hot peppers for treating or managing various health conditions looks very promising.

Diabetes
Several studies have shown that consuming chillies helps lower the heart rate and significantly reduces the amount of insulin that is required to control blood sugar levels. These benefits are more pronounced for those

individuals who have lifestyle related diabetes.

Studies done on healthy, non-diabetic individuals showed that a lesser amount of insulin was required to control blood sugar in those who consumed chillies regularly. What researchers are hoping is that chillies will be beneficial to diabetics or people who are glucose intolerant in terms of being able to control their blood sugar. If it does, it would be a simple and very cheap way to manage or prevent lifestyle-related diabetes.

Cancer
Several studies have been done and are still being done to explore the impact of capsaicin on cancer cells. H. Phillip Koeffler, professor of medicine at UCLA and director of Oncology and Hematology at Cedars-Sinai Medical Centre, has been doing extensive studies particularly on the effects of capsaicin on breast and prostate cancer.

For the research, human prostate cancer cells were placed in a laboratory dish and exposed to natural capsaicin. It was found that the capsaicin slowed down the propagation of cells dramatically - by as much as 80% According to Koeffler this is because the capsaicin triggers off a pathway that causes cell death. Further molecular tests indicated that

this is achieved by a series of events that take place inside the cell. When the capsaicin comes in contact with the cell it suppresses the release of NF-kappa B, which is a protein complex. Deficiency of NF-kappa B eventually causes the cells to self-destruct. This is a major breakthrough in treating cancer as cancer is caused by unrestrained growth of cells.

Despite this significant breakthrough, Koeffler cautions against interpreting these findings as sufficient reason to increase consumption of hot chillies if they are concerned about their high risk factor for the disease. This is because a person would need to eat about 8 of the hottest chillies in the world every week to achieve the same effect as he did in the lab.

Chillies, Blood Pressure & Health

Heart Protection: Capsaicin helps protect your heart by significantly reducing the risk factors that may lead to heart disease. Recent studies that have been done indicate that capsaicin can improve heart health by lowering blood pressure and cholesterol and preventing hardening of the arteries and clotting. Capsaicin also helps stave off inflammation, which can be a precursor to heart disease and to certain cancers.

Improved Intestinal Health: Capsaicin can help boost digestion, prevent diarrhoea, stop intestinal infections and fight Irritable Bowel Syndrome. It does this by increasing the levels of digestive fluid in the stomach. Capsaicin also helps kill bacteria that may cause infection or diarrhoea.

Improved Lung Function: Capsaicin helps to thin nasal mucus, making it easier to clear it away from the nasal passage. It also helps alleviate congestion and eases the symptoms of lung diseases such as COPD and emphysema. The effects of Capsaicin are being studied to see if this component may offer prevention for lung diseases as well. Capsaicin has antibacterial properties that help fight sinusitis and allergy symptoms.

Idiopathic rhinitis: A study done in 2009 showed that using an intranasal spray containing capsaicin significantly improved the symptoms in people with idiopathic rhinitis. People who suffer from this condition suffer from a runny nose without any obvious cause. Individuals who took 3 puffs every day of 4 mcg of the nasal spray for 3 days showed markedly improved symptoms as compared to others who took a placebo.

CHILLIES & CHOCOLATE
A DIVINE HISTORY
REDISCOVERED

"The divine drink, which builds up resistance and fights fatigue. A cup of this precious drink [cocoa] permits a man to walk for a whole day without food."

Montezuma II (1502-1520)

Chocolate! Merely say the word and millions of chocolate lovers around the world swoon in delight. Yet how many would respond in the same way when they hear "Chillies and Chocolate"?

While this may seem like an unlikely partnership, interestingly, chillies and chocolate go way back, so far back in fact that the combination was once considered the food of the gods.

In the Beginning..

According to various sources, beans of the cacao tree were allowed to ferment, then roasted and ground to create powdered chocolate known as cocoa.

Originally from Central and South America, two-thirds of today's cocoa is produced in West Africa, specifically on the Ivory Coast.

Chocolate's name is believed to have come from the word xocolatl, a word in the Aztecs' language known as Nahutal, but the history of chocolate and chillies goes back even further.

Between 250 and 900 AD, the Mayans were the first to record their use of chocolate and chillies but it was a far cry from the sweet, creamy treat we enjoy today.

They harvested, fermented, roasted and ground cocoa seeds into a paste. Then they mixed the paste with water and chilli peppers, along with spices, flavourings and other ingredients, to make a chocolate drink with a spicy kick.

By the time the Aztecs took over most of what is now Mexico and Central America, cacao seeds were so prized that they were used as money to pay tribute to the ruling empire. Aztec priests also gave cacao seeds to their gods as sacred offerings.

Enter the Aztecs

The Aztecs called their chocolate-and-chillies drink xocolatl, meaning "bitter water," because they had nothing with which to sweeten it. Even though it was bitter, chocolate with chillies was a drink of status, consumed mainly by Aztec rulers, priests and others of elite classes.

The last of the Aztec rulers, Monetzuma II "took no other beverage than the chocolatl, a potation of chocolate, flavored with vanilla and spices, and so prepared as to be reduced to a froth of the consistency of honey, which gradually dissolved in the mouth and was taken cold." William Hickling 1883

When introduced to chocolate with chillies by Spanish explorers, most Europeans found the brew too bitter. Eventually Europeans hit upon the idea of adding sugar to chocolate to sweeten it, and also of melting it and adding fats so that it would solidify. Thus was born the chocolate bar! A few hundred years later, fine chocolate confections from Switzerland, Belgium and Italy were among the world's most highly prized confectionary.

In more recent times it has become increasingly popular to add chilli back into chocolate and there are now a huge range of chilli chocolates on the market, from well known brands with a hint of chilli to full on Naga-laced concoctions.

CHILLI RECIPE

▶ Ultimate Chilli Con Carne

The definitive Chilli Con Carne recipe, for your homegrown chillies. Serves 6

Ingredients
2lbs beef mince
2 onions, chopped
2 cans kidney beans
2 cans tomatoes
4 tbsps sundried tomato paste
1 tsp sugar
6-8 garlic cloves, crushed or minced
4 Jalapeno chillies, chopped finely
2-4 Scotch Bonnets, chopped finely
5 tsps cumin seeds, toasted and crushed
3 tsps smoked paprika
2 glasses red wine
Small bunch coriander & soured cream

Method
Sear the minced beef in a very hot, heavy-based frying pan with a little olive oil, seasoning well. Once cooked through, almost to the point of burning, place to one side.

Turn the heat down to medium and fry the onion in olive oil until translucent. Add the paprika, cumin and garlic and fry for 3-4 mins. Add tomatoes, tomato paste, wine and mince.

At this point add the teaspoon of sugar, or if you feel like chilli with a twist, add a couple of squares of dark chocolate to add an extra rich flavour.

Turn the heat down very low and simmer for an hour, stirring occasionally. Then add the kidney beans and simmer for a further hour.

Add the Jalapenos and one of the minced Scotch Bonnets, cook for a few minutes and test for heat levels. Add more as required. Remember, you can always add more chillies but you can't remove them!

Cook for a further 10 mins and serve sprinkled with chopped coriander, with a dollop of soured cream and bread or rice. If you can't get soured cream, mix half natural yoghurt and half single or double cream.

▶ Salsa Verde

Aka the Green Salsa, a spicy dish with a green tomatillo base. This is served everywhere in Mexico, making a hot, fresh and aromatic addition to any Mexican meal.

Ingredients
400g tomatillos (remove outer husks)
1 small onion, diced
2 Serrano chillies (or similar green chilli such as Jalapeño)
1 clove garlic
1 tsp sugar
1 lime, juice & zest
20g coriander leaves, roughly chopped

Method
Mix the onion and lime juice and zest and set to one side. Roughly mince the tomatillos and chillies in a food processor or blender. Using a large pestle and mortar, crush the garlic into a paste with a large pinch of salt. Mix all the ingredients together and season to taste.

Tomatillos can be a bit tricky to get hold of but you can find them online in the summer months or get canned versions. Alternatively, grow your own alongside your chillies. If you really can't get hold of any tomatillos, you can replace them with green tomatoes.

▶ Habanero Jelly

Spice up your lunch with this classic recipe. A delicious hot, sweet jelly that is a perfect accompaniment to buffets, sandwiches and cold meats. Makes 6-7 1/2lb jars. Habanero Jelly makes a great gift!

Ingredients
3 red sweet peppers
5-10 Habanero chillies (or Scotch Bonnets)
12 fl oz white vinegar
3lbs caster sugar
3oz liquid fruit pectin
7 x 1/2lb jars sterilised in an oven or dishwasher

Method
Remove the stems from all the peppers as well as the sweet pepper seeds and blend together with a hand blender. Place in a very large saucepan with the sugar and vinegar and simmer for 20-30 mins.

Add the pectin and bring to a full rolling boil for 2–3 minutes. Ladle carefully into the pre-sterilised jars and seal with the lids. You can sterilise jars quickly and easily by putting them through a dishwasher cycle.

Allow to cool, label and store. A little of this jelly goes a long way!

▶ PiriPiri Prawns

This is a classic chilli recipe from Mozambique works with giant prawns or chicken. Serves 4.

Ingredients

1kg giant prawns or chicken pieces
6-12 African Devil or Birdseye chillies
2 tbsps lemon zest
3 tbsps lemon juice
10 cloves garlic, minced
2 tbsps olive oil
1/2 tsp salt
1 tsp each of paprika & dried oregano

Method

Roast the chillies for 10 mins in a medium oven. Roughly chop them, then add to a frying pan with all the ingredients, except the chicken or prawns, and simmer for 3-4 mins.

Allow to cool and blend. Rub half the mixture around the chicken or prawns and place in a covered bowl for 1 hour in the fridge.

Transfer to a roasting tray and place in a preheated oven at 200c/390f/gas 6 for 10 minutes for prawns or 30 mins for chicken, regularly basting with the left over PiriPiri chilli mixture. Serve with rice, vegetable couscous or salad.

▶ Jamaican Jerk Chicken

Delicious, aromatic Caribbean cuisine that is easy to prepare and cook. Serves 4.

Ingredients

4 chicken pieces, leg or breast (skin on)
2 Scotch Bonnets
1 tbsp brown sugar or molasses
1 tbsp olive oil
Spices (2 tsps allspice, 1/2 tsp each of nutmeg, cinnamon & paprika)
4 floz each of soy sauce & white wine vinegar
Small bunch fresh coriander and thyme
4 garlic cloves, crushed or chopped finely
2 spring onions
Juice 1 lime

Method

Blend all the ingredients, except the chicken and lime, into a smooth paste. Place the chicken in a shallow dish, cover with the sauce and marinate for a few hours or overnight.

Place the chicken under a hot grill for 20–25 mins, basting with the marinade to moisten. Don't worry if the sauce appears to blacken as the skin will protect the chicken. Once the meat has been cooked through, squeeze over the lime juice and serve with rice or Jamaican rice and peas.

▶ Shrimp Creole

Spicy seafood recipe from Louisiana. Serves 6

Ingredients
750gms large shrimp
1-2 Scotch Bonnets, finely chopped
12 spring onions & 6 shallots
6 garlic cloves, crushed
1 tspn curry powder
Small bunch flat leafed parsley &
coriander
1 tblsp grated fresh ginger
3fl oz dark rum
4 large tomatoes diced
2 tblsps tomato paste
8 floz fish stock, juice 2 limes
1 tspn sugar

Method
Fry the shallots, spring onions, chillies and garlic in a large, heavy-based frying pan on a medium heat. Add the ginger and curry powder as the onions become glassy and fry until starting to brown.

Add the tomatoes, bay leaf and half the fresh herbs, turning up the heat for a couple of minutes. Then add the rum, sugar, fish stock and tomato paste and simmer for about 10 minutes or until mixture has thickened.

In a separate bowl, marinate the shrimp in well-seasoned lime for at least half an hour and add them to the tomato mixture, simmering gently until cooked through.

Garnish with the remaining herbs and serve.

Chilli Vodka

Store in the freezer for delicious hot frozen shot or use as a base for Bloody Marys. Chilli Vodka also makes for a great homemade gift.

Ingredients
4 Habanero, or 12 Jalapeno chillies
1 litre Vodka

Method
Prick the chillies all over with a sharp skewer or quarter them if they won't fit into the bottle. Empty a little vodka out of the bottle and stuff in the chillies.

Store in a dark place for 3-4 weeks and then decant the vodka into decorative bottles, removing the chillies.

Krakatoa Hot Sauce

This mouth-blistering chilli sauce is not for the faint-hearted but it has an emphasis on flavour as well heat. Keeps well refrigerated.

Ingredients
6 - 10 fresh Naga Morichs or Bhut Jolokias
12 garlic cloves
12 spring onions
1 large carrot
3 tsps English mustard
4 floz water
6 floz chicken or vegetable stock
Juice 2 – 3 limes
Small bunch chopped coriander leaves
1 tbsp fresh chopped thyme leaves
Glass bottle sterilised in oven or dishwasher

Method
Blend the chillies, garlic, spring onions, carrot, water and stock in a food processor until smooth. Add the rest of the ingredients and pulse until thoroughly blended, adding water to get to your desired consistency.

Transfer to your pre-sterilised jar or bottle and refrigerate for at least 24 hours until the flavours have melded together. Krakatoa Hot Sauce should keep in the fridge for 6 months.

▶ Chocolate Fireballs

Aztecs made the first chocolate as a spiced drink rather than a sweet, but with these Fireballs, you can get the best of both worlds.

Ingredients
1 Habanero chilli, or 2 Birdseyes, minced
300g dark chocolate
55g caster sugar
50ml water
120ml double cream
Cocoa powder to dust

Method
Place the sugar and water in a saucepan over a low heat and stir until the sugar has dissolved.

Add the chillies and simmer for 2-3 minutes. Then turn the heat off and add the chocolate, stirring until it has melted. Stir in the cream.

Pour the mixture into a wide bowl and refrigerate until set. Roll into small balls in the palm of your hand, roll in cocoa powder and pop into sweet paper cases. Keep refrigerated and don't forget to warn people that these are hot chocolates when you offer them one!